Please and Thank You

MY FIRST MANNERS

Written by Elizabeth Clasing
Illustrated by Tom Leigh

Published by Phoenix International Publications, Inc.
8501 West Higgins Road, Suite 300, Chicago, Illinois 60631
Lower Ground Floor, 59 Gloucester Place, London W1U 8JJ

www.pikidsmedia.com

p i kids is a trademark of Phoenix International Publications, Inc., and is registered in the United States.

8 7 6 5 4 3 2 1

ISBN: 978-1-4127-6787-3

phoenix international publicat

D0009599

Monsters say "thank
Monsters say "pleas

Monsters say "excuse ME!"
Whenever monsters sneeze.

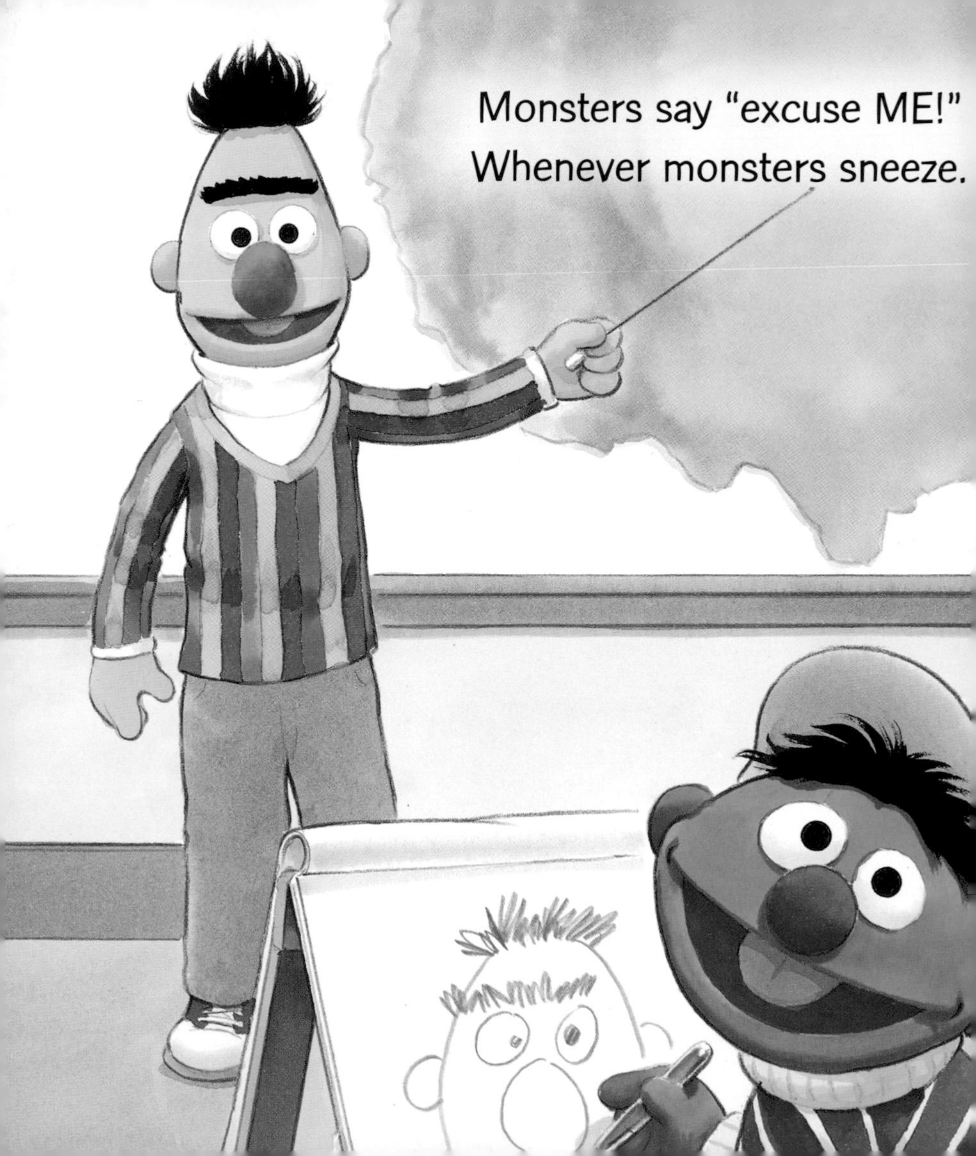

10!

Monsters take turns,
Even being "it."

Monsters at a party never take the biggest bit.

And before they get noisy...

... they'll ask if they could.

That's good manners, doing what's right.

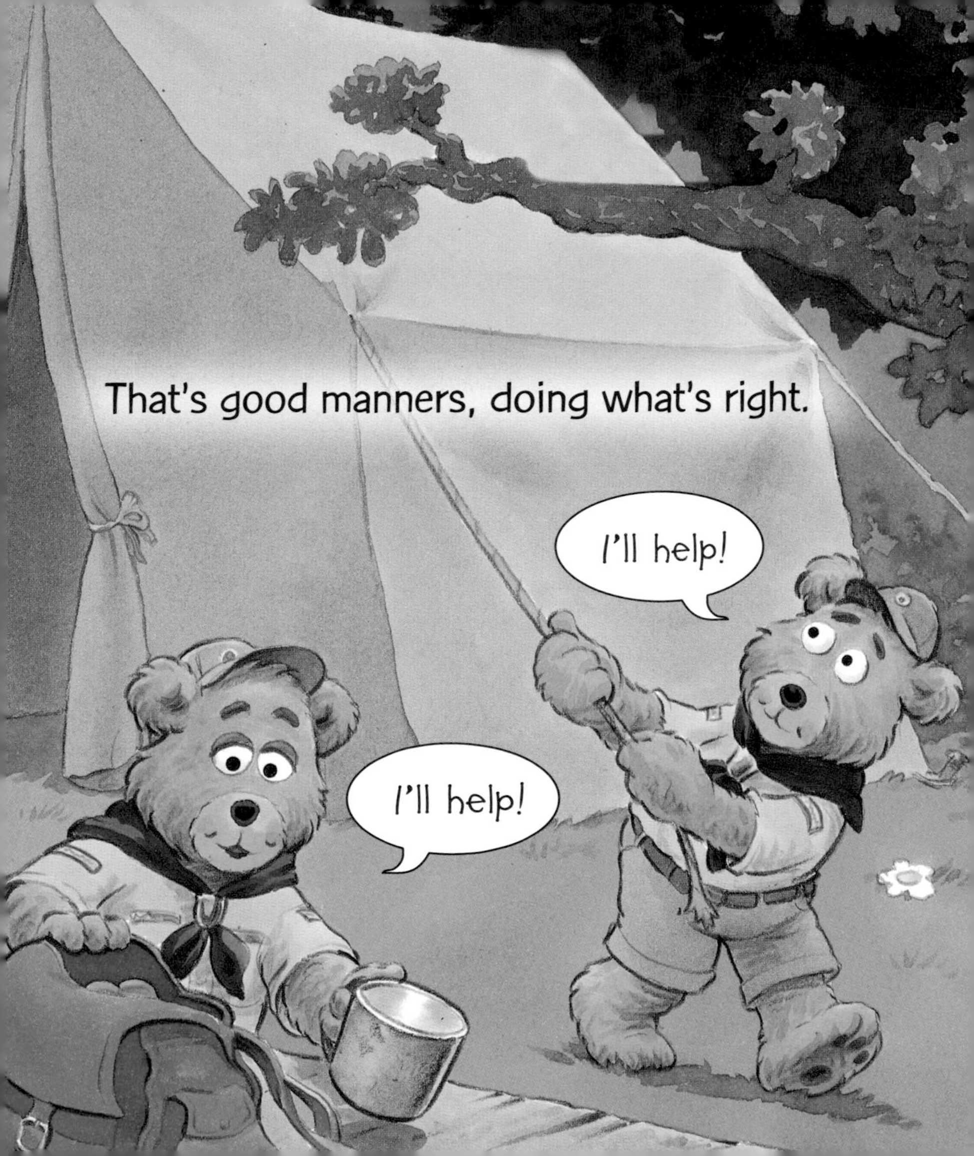